Tips for Reading Together

Children learn best when reading is fun.

- Talk about the title and the picture on the front cover.
- Identify the letter pattern *ng* in the title and talk about the sound it makes when you read it.
- Look at the *ng* and *ck* words on page 4. Say the sounds in each word and then say each word (e.g. *s-i-ng*, *sing*; *sh-o-ck*, *shock*).
- Read the story and then find the words with *ng* and *ck*.
- Talk about the story and do the fun activities at the end of the book.

Children enjoy re-reading stories and this helps to build their confidence.

Have fun!

After you have read the story, find the ten musical notes in the pictures.

The main sound practised in this book is 'ng' as in *sang*. The other sound practised is 'ck' as in *rock*.

For more hints and tips on helping your child become a successful and enthusiastic reader look at our website www.oxfordowl.co.uk.

The Sing Song

Written by Roderick Hunt
Illustrations by Nick Schon, based on
the original characters created by
Roderick Hunt and Alex Brychta

OXFORD
UNIVERSITY PRESS

Read these words

si**ng**   so**ng**

di**ng**   lo**ng**

alo**ng**   sa**ng**

ro**ck**   sho**ck**

"It is a Sing Song," said Dad.

"Let's go to the Sing Song,"
said Dad.

We can sing
a song.

"Yes, let's go along to it,"
said Mum.

They went to the Sing Song.

They met Wilf and Wilma.

Wilf and Wilma sang a song.
They had fun singing it.

Kipper had a song to sing.

Mum sang it with him.

Biff and Chip sang a song.

It was a sad song.

Dad sang a song.

It went on and on.

Dad sang and sang.

19

Dad won the Sing Song.

Talk about the story

Who did the family meet at the Sing Song?

What song did Kipper sing?

Why were Biff and Chip surprised that Dad won?

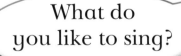

What do you like to sing?

Spot the difference

Find the five differences in the two pictures of Dad.

Read with Biff, Chip and Kipper offers two important pathways to learning to read. **First Stories** have been specially written to provide practice in reading everyday language, and the **Phonics** stories help children practise reading by decoding sounds in words, as they learn to do in school.

Books at Level 3: Becoming a reader

Look out for the next level: Developing as a reader

OXFORD
UNIVERSITY PRESS

Great Clarendon Street, Oxford OX2 6DP
Text © Roderick Hunt 2007
Illustrations © Alex Brychta and Nick Schon 2007
First published 2007. This edition published 2011
Series Advisors: Kate Ruttle, Annemarie Young

British Library Cataloguing in Publication Data available
ISBN: 978-0-19-273985-8
Printed in China by Imago
The characters in this work are the original creation of Roderick Hunt and Alex Brychta who retain copyright in the characters.
10 9 8 7 6